S0-BWD-283

Where do the Animals Go When it Rains?

This story sprang from the imaginations of my

three incredible children Henry, Jack and Sloan.

We hope to share more stories about our favorite

animals and what happens when there are

changes in the weather.

Copyright

Where Do The Animals Go When It Rains?

Copyright ©2012 by Janet Crown.

Ilustrated by Daron Rosenberg

All rights reserved. Printed in the United States of America.

FIRST EDITION

ISBN-10: 0985283009

ISBN-13: 987-0-9852830-0-1

CPSIA Compliance Information: Batch #6/12

For further information contact RJ Communications, NY NY, 800-621-2556.

Where do the Animals Go When it Rains?

This book is dedicated to my wonderful children, Henry, Jack & Sloan. I love you to pieces. You are my greatest gift. And, special thanks to my two step daughters, Tara and Alexa, for your tolerance, loving support and ability to rhyme.

And special, special thanks to the love of my life-my rock, my brilliant, handsome, thoughtful, wonderful, patient, tolerant husband-Steve. You inspire me every day to be the best that I can be. You are my best friend. Without you, this book would never have seen the light of day.

Proceeds from this book are donated to
The Painted Turtle www.thepaintedturtle.org

When the
sky turns gray,
and suddenly it becomes
a rainy day,
where do all the animals go
when they can't
run around and play?

The **bear** lopes into his cave and snuggles **next to a rock,** while he listens to the rain tick like a **grandfather clock.**

The **squirrel** scampers up

a big **oak tree,**

looking frantically for a branch

large enough to protect his

entire family.

The **rabbits** disappear
into the tall
grass and flowers,
huddling close
to keep warm,
in the cold
windy showers.

The **deer** burrow in the woods **without making a sound,** protecting each other, as the **rain trickles down.**

The **horses** race back to the dark **red barn,** to protect the young phillies and colts so they do not wander out into **any harm.**

The **birds** soar through the sky to find their **nests,** where they finally relax, and give their wings **a rest.**

Then **frogs** begin jumping
from the shore
to the **lily pads.**

They love the rain, it's like
a party with **the fish.**
How could they possibly
be mad?

Finally mother and baby **mouse** hide out under the **house,** while the brother's frolic **in the rain,** waiting patiently for the sun to **shine again.**

About the Author

Janet Crown currently lives in Los Angeles with her husband, Steve Robinson and her children Henry, Jack, Sloan, and step daughters, Alexa and Tara. Born and raised in Wilmette, Illinois, Janet is the seventh child of Renee and Lester Crown and the aunt to 25 nieces and nephews. She is a graduate of Denison University and Northwestern University's Medill School of Journalism.

Janet is involved in several leading non-profit organizations including The Painted Turtle, where she is a founding member. *Where Do The Animals Go When It Rains* is her first title in a series of children's books. All proceeds from this book will be donated to **The Painted Turtle** http://www.thepaintedturtle.org

The Painted Turtle is where children with chronic and life threatening medical conditions celebrate just being kids! Through innovative, camp-based programs that offer a great big dose of fun and support, children with more than 30 medical conditions visit The Painted Turtle each year. A member of Paul Newman's formerly Hole in the Wall Camps, The Painted Turtle has offered thousands of children and their families hope and encouragement through its Summer and Family Weekend camps since it opened its gates in 2004. There is no billing department at The Painted Turtle—campers and their families attend free of charge.

About the Illustrator

Daron Rosenberg currently lives in northern New Jersey with his wonderful wife Stacy and two beautiful daughters, Phoebe and Sloane. Phoebe is at the age now when cuddling up before bedtime with her parents and a good children's book is great family time and the only way to go to sleep. Sloane will soon follow her big sister's lead.

After 12 years of designing for magazines, in 2001 Daron started his own design & marketing business, Daron Rosenberg Creative LLC. He graduated from the University of Michigan Art School with a BFA and took advanced studies at the School of Visual Arts, The Art Students League of NY and the New York Studio School.

More of his work can be seen at http://www.daronrosenberg.com